GROWING UP

SENIOR AUTHORS
Virginia A. Arnold
Carl B. Smith

LITERATURE CONSULTANTS
Joan I. Glazer
Margaret H. Lippert

READING
EXPRESS
MACMILLAN

Macmillan Publishing Company
New York

Collier Macmillan Publishers
London

Macmillan Publishing Company
866 Third Avenue
New York, N.Y. 10022
Collier Macmillan Canada, Inc.

Printed in the United States of America

ISBN 0-02-160040-6

9 8 7 6 5 4 3

ACKNOWLEDGMENTS

The publisher gratefully acknowledges permission to reprint the following copyrighted material:

"The Clown" by Dorothy Aldis is reprinted from HOP, SKIP AND JUMP! by Dorothy Aldis. Copyright 1934, copyright renewed © 1961 by Dorothy Aldis. Reprinted by permission of G.P. Putnam's Sons.

"Space Swing" by Margaret Hillert from FARTHER THAN FAR by Margaret Hillert. Used by permission of the author who controls all rights.

"Stop-Go" by Dorothy Baruch is from I LIKE AUTOMOBILES by Dorothy Baruch. Copyright 1931, copyright renewed. Reprinted by permission of Bertha Klausner International Literary Agency, Inc.

Cover Design: Bass and Goldman Associates

Illustration Credits: Don Almquist, 26–35; June Ottani Baensh, 18–19; Eric Barnes, 36–37, 134; Olivia Cole, 154–170; Gwen Connelly, 10–16; Len Ebert, 106–115; Fred Harsh, 76–85; Sal Murdocca, 57–65; John Nez, 152–153; Stephen Peringer, 54–55; Bob Shein, 66–73; Jerry Smath, 38–45, 94–103; Sally Springer, 116–125; Chuck Wimmer, 136–151.

Cover Photo: The Image Bank: © Joseph B. Brignolo

Photo Credits: © George Ancona, 20–25. Art Resource: © D.W. Funt, 131T; © Eugene Luttenbert, 129T. Black Star: © Richard Howard, 50; © Len Kaufman, 48, 52. © Michael Heron, 74. Duomo Photography, Inc.: © Dan Helms, 129B. The Image Bank: © Nancy Brown, 130TR; © Lawrence Fried, 128L; © Robert Lee II, 130TC; © Chuck Place, 49. International Stock Photography: © Mimi Cotter, 132B. © Barbara Kirk, 88–93. © Brent Jones, 128TC. Magnum Photos: © Richard Kalvar, 130TL. Monkmeyer Press Photo Service: © Irene Bayer, 128B; © Paul Conklin, 132(inset); © J. Cron, 51. Photo Researchers, Inc.: © Junebug Clark, 105; © Ringling Bros.–Barnum & Bailey Combined Shows, Inc., 8; © Suzanne Szasz, 128TR. Picture Group: © Stephen R. Brown, 132TL. Shostal Associates: © Claude Shostal, 104. Stock, Boston: © Denley Darlson, 131B.

Contents

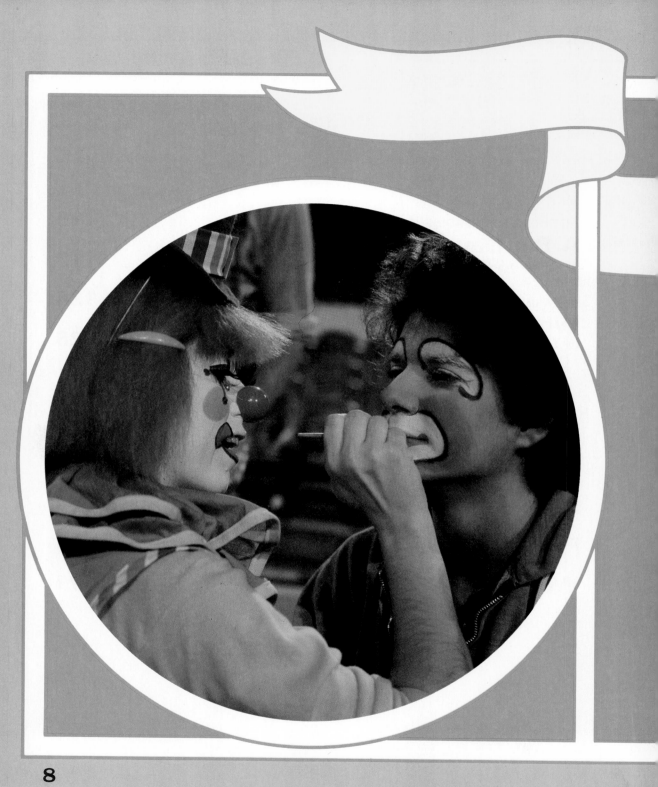

8

UNIT ONE

LEVEL 4

CIRCUS
FRIENDS

PREPARING FOR READING

Learning Vocabulary

Listen.

girl   ball

Read.

1. I read in <u>school</u>.
2. My <u>friend</u> and I play, too.
3. My friend likes to play with <u>me</u>.
4. I <u>am</u> happy at school.

school   friend   me   am

Developing Background
Read and talk.

Play at School
My friend and I like to play at school.
I am Kim, and my friend is Sue.
We like to run and kick a ball.
We like to ride up and down.
We like to play a quiet game, too.

A FRIEND AT SCHOOL

Anne Miranda

Sue and Kim like to play at school.
Sue and Kim like to kick the ball
at school.
"Kick the ball to me," said Sue.
"I can get the ball."

"Look where the ball is!" said Sue.

"We have to get the ball down," said Kim.

"Who can help get the ball down?" asked Sue.

"Anne can help me," Kim said.
"Anne is big, and she is my friend.
We can get Anne."

13

"Anne, can you get the ball down for
my friend and me?" asked Kim.

"I can help you," said Anne.
"Where is the ball? Show me!"

"We can show you," said Kim and Sue.

"That is where it is!
I see the ball!" said Anne.
"I am big, but I can't get that ball."

"We have to get it!" said Sue.

"I can jump, but I can't jump
to get that ball," said Anne.

"Can you get the ball with
your bat?" asked Kim.

15

"My bat!" said Anne.
"I can get your ball with my bat."

"Look out!" said Anne

"You did it!" said Kim.

Sue said, "I am happy now.
We can play."

"You are a big help, Anne," said Kim.
"I am happy that you are my friend."

"I like to help you," said Anne.
"I am happy to help a friend
at school."

Questions

Read and think.

1. Where did Kim and Sue like
   to play?

2. Where did Kim kick the ball?

3. Who did Kim and Sue get to help?

PREPARING FOR READING

Learning Vocabulary

Listen.

book

Read.

1. The boy and girl <u>work</u> at school.
2. <u>They</u> like to work at school.
3. <u>First</u> they <u>will</u> read.
4. Now they <u>stop</u> to play a game.

work   they   first   will   stop

School

A school is where you work and play.
That boy and girl go to school.
At school, they will read a book,
but they will play a game, too.
They stop work to help with the pets.
The boy and girl like to go to school.

MY SCHOOL

Sally Senzell

I like to go to school.
I work and play at school.
I will see my friend Tim at school.
I will see my friend Jane.
They go to school, too.

20

I walk out to get on the bus.
My cat and dog run out with me.
They can't go to school with me.
They will have to stop at the bus.
A cat and a dog can't go to school.

Now I am in school.
We have fish at school.
They are the school pets.
Fish are pets that you can't pet.

First we read at school.
It is quiet where we read.
I will read a book to my
friend Jane.
Jane will read a book to me.

22

We work and play at school.
I like to work at school, but I like
to play, too.
We have to stop work now.
We have to go now.

My bus is the first bus to go.
It will stop at my house.

I get on the bus.
I will ride to the first stop.
My house is at the first stop.
My cat and dog run out to see me.

I like to go to school.
Do you?

Questions

Read and think.

1. Where does the boy like to go?

2. Who will the boy see at school?

3. Who can't go to school with the boy?

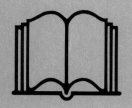

PREPARING FOR READING

Learning Vocabulary

Listen.

bus

Read.

1. I <u>must</u> <u>write</u> to my friend.
2. My friend will like to get a <u>letter</u>.
3. First I must write "<u>Dear</u> friend" on my letter.
4. I must <u>mail</u> my letter, too.

must   write   letter   dear   mail

Developing Background
Read and talk.

A Letter

I am José.
I must write a letter for school.
First I write the letter to Bob.
Now, where do I mail it?
Where does my letter go first?
Who will get my letter to Bob?

A Friend in the Country

Susan Alberghini

I must write a letter for school.
I will write to Bob.
Bob is in the country.
I am in the city.
Will I like Bob?
Will he like me?

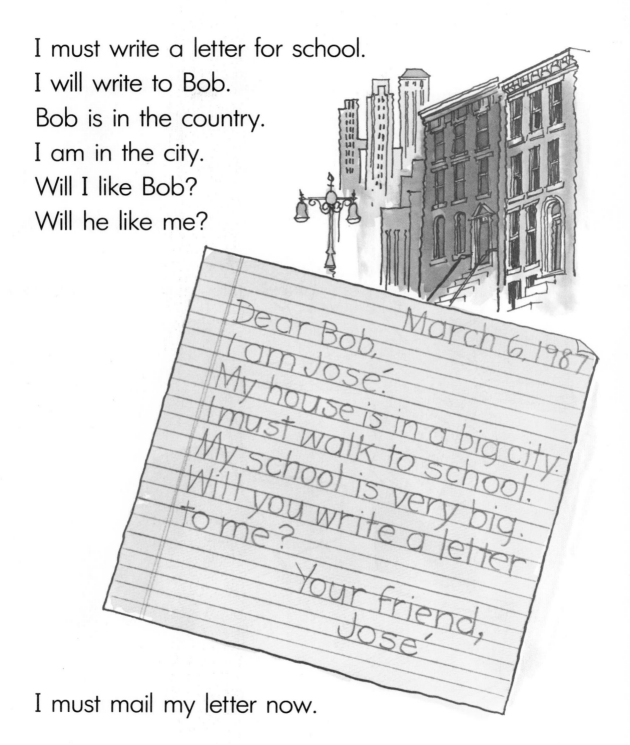

March 6, 1987
Dear Bob,
I am José.
My house is in a big city.
I must walk to school.
My school is very big.
Will you write a letter
to me?
        Your friend,
        José

I must mail my letter now.

Bob did write a letter to me!

Dear José, March 15, 1987

My house is in the country.
I must ride to school
on a bus.
I like to read at school.
I like to play, too.
Do you have pets?
Write to me.
I like to get a letter
in the mail.
            Your friend,
            Bob

31

March 25, 1987

Dear Bob,

I have a pet.

My pet is a cat.

I like to play ball.

In the city, we must play ball in the park.

Do you like to play ball, too?

Your friend,
José

32

March 31, 1987

Dear José,

I do like to play ball.
We play at a park in
the country, too.
I like to ride my pet.
My pet is a little pony.
Can you ride the bus
to the country to
see me?

Your friend,
Bob

Bob and I write and write.
I mail a letter to Bob.
I like to have Bob mail a letter to me.
I like Bob, and Bob likes me.
I have a friend in the country now.

Questions

Read and think.

1. Who likes to write to Bob?

2. Who rides to school on a bus?

3. Who can have a pony for a pet?

WRITING ACTIVITY

WRITE A LETTER

Prewrite

José likes to write a letter to Bob.
You can write a letter to a friend, too.

Look at the pets.
Write sentences for a pet you like.

Look for words in the Picture Dictionary
in your book.
Write your sentences on your paper.

I have a pet.
My pet is a _____.
My pet is _____.
My pet can _____ and _____.

Write

Now you will write your letter.

May 17, 19___

Dear _____,
  I have a pet.
  _____
  _____

      Your friend,

  _____

1. Write the letter on your paper.
2. Write the sentences on page 36
   in your letter.
3. Read your letter.
   It should say what your pet is like.

PREPARING FOR READING

Learning Vocabulary

Listen.

Read.

1. My friend and I go to the <u>circus</u>.
2. My friend is a <u>giraffe</u>.
3. He will <u>not</u> <u>sit</u> with me.
4. <u>Then</u> I am not happy.

circus   giraffe   not   sit   then

Developing Background

Read and talk.

A Circus School

Who likes to go to school?
Giraffe and Pony do.
They go to a circus school.
At circus school, you do not sit.
You must jump, run, and ride.
First you work, and then you play.

A CIRCUS SCHOOL

Jerry Smath

Giraffe rides to school in a bus.
Pony rides in the bus, too.
They do not go to a school where
they read and write.
Giraffe and Pony are in the circus.
They go to a circus school.

At the circus school they work and play.
"I like my work.
Look at me!" calls Pony.
"I can run and jump on the big ball.
First I will ride on the ball,
and then I will stop.
Look at me on the big ball!" she calls.

41

"Look at me!" calls Giraffe.
"I am happy with my work, too.
I can sit in the plane and ride.
First I go up,
and then I go down.
Look at me sit and ride!" he calls.
"Look at me ride up and down!"

42

Kitten looks at Giraffe and Pony.
She is not happy.
She is sad.
She does not go to the circus school.

"Can I work with you in the circus?"
she says to Giraffe.
"I like the circus."

"Then do not sit and look," he says.
"Get in and sit with me."

Now Kitten is happy at the circus school.
First she rides in the plane with Giraffe.
Then she rides on the ball with Pony.

"Look at me!" she calls.
"Now I am in the circus school, too."

Questions

Read and think.

1. Where do Giraffe and Pony go
   to school?

2. Who can run and jump?

3. Where does Kitten ride?

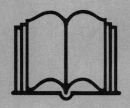

PREPARING FOR READING

Learning Vocabulary

Listen.

u<u>p</u>

Read.

1. The dog rides on <u>top</u> <u>of</u> the car.
2. The dog can run <u>or</u> walk.
3. <u>Day</u> or <u>night</u>, you can see the dog.
4. He is in the <u>tent</u> at the circus.

top   of   or   day   night   tent

Developing Background

Read and talk.

The Circus

People like to see a circus.
The circus is in a big tent.
People work at the circus.
See that woman ride and jump.
See that man work with a
big cat.
People work day and night
at the circus.

A DAY AT THE CIRCUS

Anne Rockwell

The people are at the circus.
They like to see the show at the circus.
The circus is in a tent.

Is it day or is it night?
It is day, but it looks like night.
The show will go on day or night.

The people look at the man and woman.
That man and woman work in the circus.
They work in the circus day and night.
It looks like play, but it is work.

The people look at a big dog and a little dog.
The big dog can work with the woman.
Look at that!
That dog can jump!
The dog can jump on top.
The people like to see the dog jump.

Now the people look up to
the top of the tent.
A woman is at the top of the tent.
A man is with the woman at the top.
Will the woman jump?
The woman does jump!
Look at the man and woman
ride up and down.

52

Do the people at the circus
look happy or sad?
The people at the circus look happy.
The people like the circus.
Big or little, girl or boy—
people like a circus.

Questions

Read and think:

1. Where do people see a
   circus show?

2. Who is at the top of the tent?

3. Who likes the circus?

THE CLOWN

I like to see
The spotted clown
Throwing dishes
In the air.
When they've started
Coming down
He looks as though
He didn't care,
But catches each one
Perfectly,
Over and over,
Every time,
One and two and
One-two-three—
Like a pattern
Or a rhyme.

Dorothy Aldis

PREPARING FOR READING

Learning Vocabulary

Listen.

-ed	-ing
walk	look
walk<u>ed</u>	look<u>ing</u>

Read.

1. The woman <u>walked</u> out of the zoo.
2. She <u>was</u> <u>looking</u> up and down.
3. "<u>What</u> are you looking for?" a man asked.
4. "Where is the <u>last</u> bus to the city?" she asked.

walked   was   looking   what   last

Developing Background
Read and talk.

What? Where? Who?

I was looking for my dog in the park.
I asked my friend for help.
She asked, "What does your dog
look like?
Where did you see your dog last?
Who was in the park with you?"

Was my friend a help to me?

Where Are You?

Jim Razzi

It was night at the circus.
The man was looking for a bird.
He asked the woman, "Did you see
a bird?"

The woman asked, "What does the bird look like?"

"It is a very big bird," said the man.

"I did not see it," said the woman. "Where did you see it last? I will help you look for it."

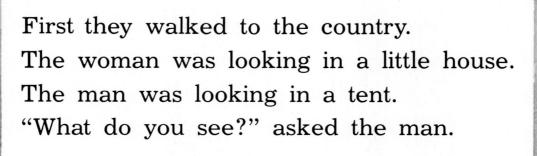

First they walked to the country.
The woman was looking in a little house.
The man was looking in a tent.
"What do you see?" asked the man.

"I see a dog but not a bird,"
said the woman.

"Where does a bird go at night?"
asked the man.

Then the man and the woman walked
to the park.
It was very quiet.
The woman was looking up and down.
The man was looking on top of a car.
The man asked the woman,
"What do you see?"

"I see a cat but not a bird,"
said the woman.

"What does that bird do at night?"
asked the man.

At last, the man and woman walked
to the city.
They asked people to help look
for the bird.

"I can't help you," said a boy.
"I have to go to school."

"I can't look for it now," said a woman.
"I have to go to work."

At last, a little girl asked,
"Does the bird have a friend?"

"It does have a friend," said the man.
"The bird likes the giraffe."

"Then that is where you must look
for the bird," said the little girl.

The man and woman walked to the circus.
They walked to the house of the giraffe.

"I see the bird at last!"
said the woman.

"Now I see where you go at night,"
said the man.
"I see what you do.
You like to sit with your friend."

Questions

Read and think.

1. Where did the man and woman walk first?

2. Who was a big help to the man and woman?

3. Where did the bird go at night?

PREPARING FOR READING

Learning Vocabulary

Listen.

top

Read.

1. The giraffe liked <u>spots</u>.
2. He was looking in the <u>water</u>.
3. "Can fish <u>grow</u> <u>some</u> spots?"
   he asked.
4. "Who <u>paints</u> spots on fish?"
   he asked.

spots   water   grow   some   paints

Developing Background

Read and talk.

Spots! Spots! Spots!

What are some pets that have spots?
Does that fish in the water have spots?
Where are the spots on the fish?
Where is a little pet with some spots?
What is it?
Look for a big pet with spots.
What is it?

The Sad Little Giraffe

Margaret H. Lippert

A little giraffe was looking
in the water.
He was sad.
He liked spots.
He did not have spots.

He said, "Fish, where are you?
Jump out of the water and show me
your spots."

68

Fish did jump out of the water.
He said, "Look at my spots. I have some
big spots and some little spots."

Giraffe asked, "Who paints spots?
Where can I get some?"

Fish said, "Mouse paints spots.
She paints little spots, and she paints
big spots."

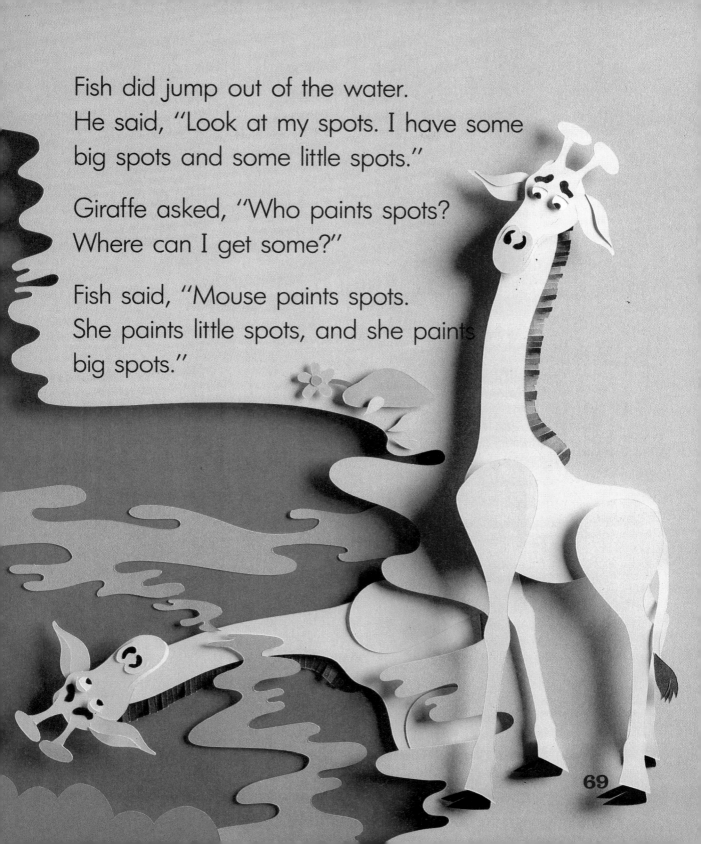

Giraffe walked to see Mouse.
Giraffe said, "Mouse, can I have
some big spots?
I am big, and I like big spots."

Mouse said, "I will work on
some spots for you."

Mouse liked to work.
Mouse walked to the top of Giraffe.
"I will work day and night," she said.

Then Mouse asked Giraffe, "Do you like your spots?"

Giraffe said, "STOP! My spots are too little.
I said I liked big spots!"

Mouse said, "You will grow, and your
spots will grow.
They will grow very big."

72

Then Giraffe was happy.
He walked to the water.

"I like my spots," he said.
"They are not big now, but they will
grow very big."

Questions

Read and think.

1. What did Giraffe like that he did
   not have?

2. Where did Giraffe go to get
   some spots?

3. Did Giraffe like big spots or little spots?

UNIT TWO   LEVEL 4

WHAT WILL
I BE?

PREPARING FOR READING

Learning Vocabulary

Listen.

<u>g</u>reen

Read.

1. I like <u>green</u> paints.
2. The <u>sky</u> is <u>blue</u>, but I paint it green.
3. I paint <u>pretty</u> green <u>pictures</u>.
4. <u>May</u> I paint you?

green   sky   blue   pretty
pictures   may

Developing Background
Read and talk.

Looking at Pictures
Jim likes to paint pretty pictures.
He likes to go and see pictures, too.
Jim likes to see pictures like
"The Circus."
"Look at the red and blue," he says.
"I may paint like that some day."

THE BLUE ZOO

Anne Miranda

"Look at what was in
the mail!" said Jim.
"It is for me."
Jim read the letter.

"My friend Sally says the paints
are for me.
Now I can paint pretty pictures
at school!" said Jim.
"I can paint pretty pictures for
you, too."

Jim walked to school with the paints.
"Mr. Park, look at my paints!" said Jim.

"Your paints are pretty," said Mr. Park.
"We will paint zoo pictures now.
Your paints will help you.
You can do a pretty sky with your
blue paints."

Some of the people at school liked
the paints.
"May I have some green?" asked Linda.

"Me, too!" said David.

"May I have the red?" asked Maria.
Ken asked for red, too.

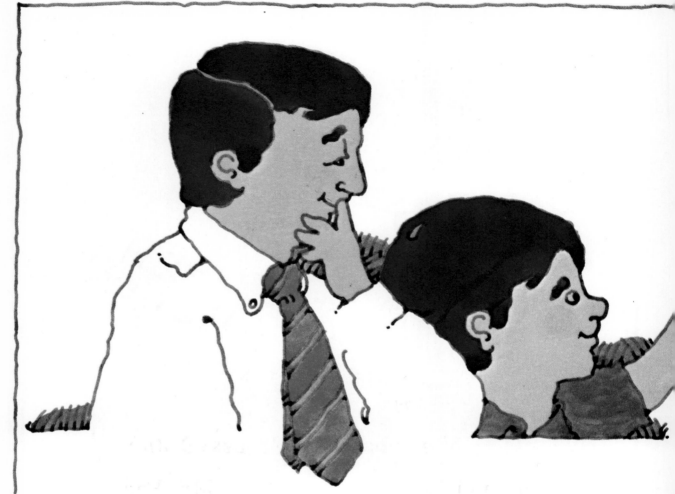

"You may have some of my paints,"
said Jim.
"But now I do not have paints
for me.
I have blue, and that is that.
I will have to paint my zoo blue."

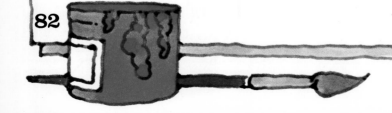

"May I see your pictures now?"
asked Mr. Park.

"Do you like what I did?" asked Jim.

"Jim, your zoo is blue!" said Mr. Park.
"You have a blue sky, and I like
your blue sky.
Your pony is blue like the sky, too.
The water is blue, but your fish are
blue, too!
Do you not like green or red?"

"I do like green, but I do not have green," said Jim.
"Linda and David have my green paints. Maria and Ken have the red."

84

"I like your blue zoo," said Mr. Park.
"It is top work!
I will show it to some people
in school."

Jim was happy now.
Mr. Park did like the blue zoo!

Questions

Read and think.

1. What did Jim get in the mail?

2. What did Jim do with the green and red paints?

3. What did Jim paint with the blue paint?

PREPARING FOR READING

Learning Vocabulary

Listen.

drum

Read.

1. Can you drive a truck?
2. My mother and father drive a big truck.
3. At night, they sleep in the truck.

drive   truck   mother   father   sleep

Developing Background
Read and talk.

The Truck Stop

I like a truck stop.
The people in the green truck work
in the park.
See the mail truck.
You can sleep in that little truck.
The people in the red truck work
for the city.

87

A TRUCK RIDE

Barbara Kirk

My mother and father work.
They drive a big truck.
It is work that they like.
My father calls the truck Big Blue.

88

I am happy now that school is out.
Now I can go in Big Blue, too!
We will drive a truck of fish to the city.

My father helps me get in the truck.
He says that my dog Fred can ride, too.

Now Mother, Father, Fred, and I
ride in Big Blue.
We ride in the day.
We ride in the night, too.

Mother likes to drive first.
We ride, and ride, and ride.

I have my paints with me.
I paint pictures of what I see.
First the sky is big and blue.
Now the sky looks red.

Now it is night, and we have to sleep.
But we do not stop to sleep.
We can sleep in the truck.
Mother and I will get some sleep, and
Father will drive.

We stop at a truck stop and go in.
We see a friend of my father.
Then we go out.
Mother looks at the fish.
Now we drive on.

At last we get to the city.
We park the truck and get out.

The people are happy to get the fish.
We are happy, too.

I like to work with Mother, Father, and Big Blue.

Questions

Read and think.

1. What did Father call the truck?

2. What was in the truck?

3. Who likes to drive first?

PREPARING FOR READING

Learning Vocabulary

Listen.

plane

Read.

1. A blue truck <u>came</u> to my house.
2. "May I take <u>one</u> ride in it?"
   I asked.
3. "You may take <u>two</u> rides,"
   said Father.
4. "<u>Why</u> <u>don't</u> we ride now?"
   asked Mother.

came   one   two   why   don't

Developing Background
Read and talk.

Sam Paints Pictures

I am Sam the car.

I paint one or two pictures a day.

See the pictures of my mother and
father.

That bird and fish are a big help
to me.

I like to paint pictures.

SAM
THE CAR

Jerry Smath

"May I go out and work with Father?"
asked Sam the car.

"You may not," said Mother.

"Why can't I work, too?" he asked.
"Why can't I work in the city with Father?"

"Some day you will," she said.
"Now you must go out and play."

Sam is sad, but he does what Mother says.

Sam was looking up in the sky.
A bird was in the sky.

"Why can't I go up in the sky with you?"
Sam asked.

"Don't look sad," said the bird.
"You don't have to.
Look at what you can do!
One, you can go.
Two, you can stop."

Sam was looking down in the water.
A fish was in the water.

"Why can't I go in the water with you?"
asked Sam.

"Don't look sad," said the fish.
"You don't have to.
Look at what you can do!
One, you can drive up.
Two, you can drive down."

The bird in the sky said,
"I see a car.
It is your father, Sam."

Sam the car was very happy.
"Why is he not in the city?" asked Sam.
"Why is he not at work now?"

Father came up to Sam.

"I came to get you," said Father.

"I came for your help.

The bus in the city can't run now.

People must have rides."

"You must drive to the city," said Father.

"Your mother can't go.

She says that you may help.

Show me what you can do."

Sam said, "I will! I will!"

"One, I can stop and go.
Two, I can drive up and down."
Sam asked, "May we go now, Father?"

Father said, "We can."

Sam came to the city with Father.
"We are happy to see you," said the people.

"I am happy that you came," said Father.

"Me, too!" said Sam.
"I like to drive with you.
One, we can stop and go.
Two, we can drive up and down."

What a day for Sam the car!

Questions

Read and think.

1. Where did Father work?

2. What can Sam do to help
   the people?

3. Where did Sam and Father go?

STOP-GO

Automobiles
In
    a
       row
Wait to go
While the signal says:
          STOP

Bells ring
Tingaling
Red light's gone!
Green light's on!
Horns blow!
And the row
Starts
    to
           GO

Dorothy W. Baruch

PREPARING FOR READING

Learning Vocabulary

Listen.

kick

Read.

1. We <u>pick</u> <u>apples</u> in the country.
2. We work on a <u>farm</u>.
3. We <u>put</u> the apples in a <u>box</u>.
4. Then we <u>take</u> the box to the truck.

pick   farm   put   box   take   apples

106

Developing Background
Read and talk.

At Play on the Farm
My friend came to the farm.
"What can we play?" she asked.
"We can pick apples," I said.
"You can take a ride on a pony.
We can sleep out in my tent.
That is some of what we can do!"

107

ON THE FARM

Judy Davis

It is quiet on the farm.
Father will get up to work.
I get up to work, too.

Father calls me, and we go out.
I take my red box with me.
It helps me work on the farm.

First we sit down with Bessie.
She is happy to see Father and me.
Father helps me work with Bessie.

Then I take my box to Mabel.
I like Mabel, but she can kick!

"Look out!" says Father.
"You must sit where Mabel can't
kick you."

Now I get some water for Little Red.
He is my pony and my friend.
I put the water where he can get to it.

Then I take Little Red out for a walk.
Then we go for a ride.

Now Father calls to me,
"You must help me pick apples.
Take your box with you.
Put it on the truck."

Then we drive out to pick apples.
Father says, "You can pick some apples.
Don't pick green apples.
Green apples must get red first."

"We can stop work now," says Father.
"You have put in a big day.
You are a big help on the farm."

I put my box up on the truck.
Father and I drive to the house.

I like to help on the farm.

Questions

Read and think.

1. What can Mabel do?

2. Who is Little Red?

3. What can you pick on a farm?

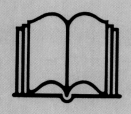

PREPARING FOR READING

Learning Vocabulary

Listen.

a girl   a girl's book

Read.

1. My <u>teacher's</u> pictures are pretty.
2. He <u>teaches</u> me to paint pictures, too.
3. My <u>teacher</u> sits and paints with me.
4. Then we take <u>time</u> and look at my work.

teacher's   teaches   teacher   time

Developing Background
Read and talk.

Your Teacher
What does your teacher do?
Your teacher teaches you to read.
Your teacher will take time to help
you look for a book.
Your teacher helps you write a letter.
Your teacher is a friend.

A Big Day at School

Susan Alberghini

I am Pamela, but my mother calls me Pam.
My mother is a teacher.

One day, she says I can go to school, too.
We will go to the school where
she teaches.

118

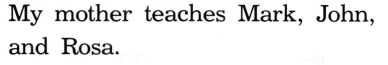

My mother teaches Mark, John,
and Rosa.
My mother teaches Lisa, too.

Lisa can't walk like I can walk.
Lisa can't walk, but she can read.

My mother sits down and helps Lisa
and John read.
My mother looks at a teacher's book.
The teacher's book helps my mother.

Now it is time to play.
Lisa says she will show me a game.
She helps me get the game out of the
teacher's box.
Then she sits and teaches me
the game.

Lisa is the teacher now.
She teaches me to play the game.

"It is time to work on pictures,"
says Mother.
"Your pictures must show a friend."

Lisa sits and paints two pictures.
One is of John, and one is of me!

"What pretty pictures!" says Mother.
"But we must stop work now.
It is time to go out and play."

Rosa says, "What can we do?"

"Some of you can run.
Some of you can play ball,"
says Mother.

Lisa says, "Pam, you can play ball
with me."

Lisa can play ball!
She can't walk, but she can play ball!

Look at that!
The ball is in!
That was the first ball to go in,
and Lisa put it in!
I am happy for my friend Lisa.

It is time for the bus now.
That is the bus that Lisa will ride.
That bus can help Lisa get on.

Lisa sits and looks out at me.
"Pam," she calls.
"Your mother is my teacher, but you
are my friend."

I am happy that Lisa is my friend.
I am happy that my mother is
a teacher.
What a big day at school for
the teacher's little girl.

Questions

Read and think.

1. Where did Pam and Mother go?

2. What can Lisa do?

3. Who did Lisa paint pictures of?

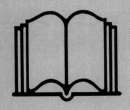

PREPARING FOR READING

Learning Vocabulary

Listen.

truck

Read.

1. I help people take trips.
2. Some people like to go up in the air, so they take a plane.
3. Some people live in a truck when they go on trips.
4. I will be happy to help you.

trips   air   so   live   when   be

Developing Background
Read and talk.

Who Are You?

Who are you?
Where do you live?
Where do you go to school?
What will you be when you grow up?
You can't say now what you will be.
You will say when you grow up.

When You Grow Up

Loretta Kaim

What will you be when you grow up?

Will you do work like your father?

Will you do work like your mother?

What will you do?

I will play ball for my work.
I will play ball in a big park.

I will bat the ball up in the air.
Up, up in the air it will go.
My ball will look like a bird in
the air.
My ball will go like a plane in
the air.
One day, my ball will go out of the
park, and people will be so happy.

When I grow up, I will have a
big bus.
I will live in the city.
A man will drive the bus.

People will take trips on my bus.
They will take trips,
so they can see the city.
They will take trips,
so they can see the country.
People will be very happy to
take my trips.

I will help with the mail when I grow up.
I will live in the country and take
mail to people.

I will ride in my little truck.
I will take the mail with me.

I will ride up to a box, so I can
put the mail in.
Then the people will take
the mail out.
I will be happy to see people,
and they will be happy to see me.

T.P. 35

What will I be when I grow up?
I can't say.
I may live and work in the city.
I may live and work in the country.

I may be a father.
I may be a teacher.
I may be a father and a teacher.

What will I be when I grow up?
I can't say now.
I don't have to say now.
I am not so very big now.

Questions

Read and think.

1. Why will people take trips on the bus?

2. What will the girl do to help with the mail?

3. What will you be when you grow up?

WRITING ACTIVITY

WRITE SENTENCES

Prewrite

What will you be when you grow up?
Kim says she will work on a farm.
Read Kim's sentences.

I am Kim.
I will work on my farm when I grow up.
I will grow apples on my farm.
Then I will pick my apples and
put the apples in a truck.
I will drive to the city with
the apples.
I will like my farm.

Pick what you will be when you grow up.
Your teacher will help you write
your sentences.

Write

1. Write the sentences on your paper.
2. Look for words in the Picture Dictionary in your book.
3. Write a sentence that says who you are.
4. Then write a sentence that says what you will be.
5. Last, write sentences that say what you will do.
6. Read your sentences.
   Do they say what you will be and do when you grow up?

PREPARING FOR READING

Learning Vocabulary

Listen.

sl<u>ee</u>p

Read.

1. Have you <u>seen</u> the <u>funny</u> plane?

2. We <u>were</u> happy to see it <u>fly</u>.

3. We may take <u>three</u> trips in it.

seen   funny   were   fly   three

Developing Background

Read and talk.

A Letter

March 8, 1987

Dear Jim,

    We put on a play at my school.
I was Cathy, a girl who liked to fly.
She and a friend, Bart, go to a
funny country.
My mother said that it was
some play!

Your friend,
Sally

SKY RIDE

Lorenca Consuelo Rosal

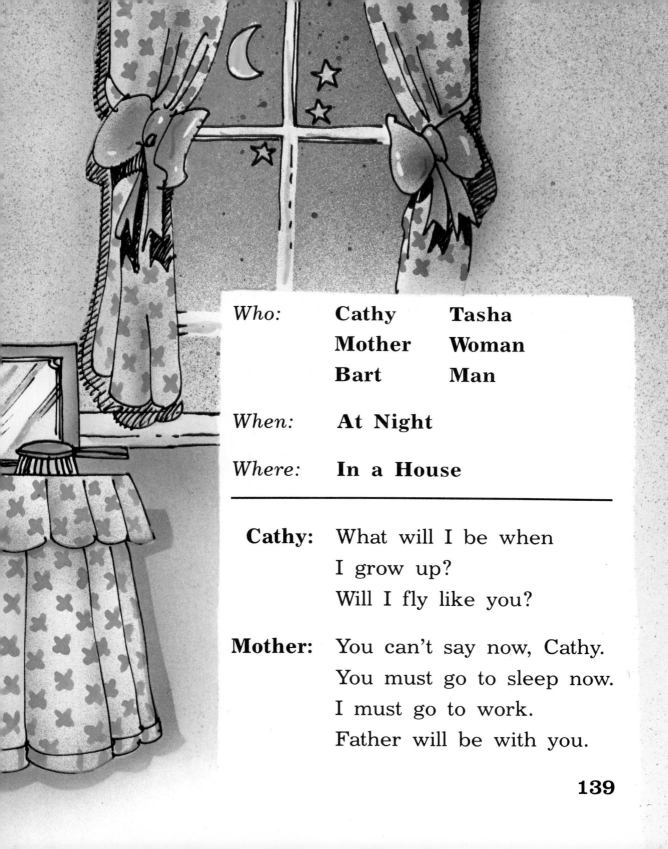

Who:	Cathy	Tasha
	Mother	**Woman**
	Bart	**Man**

When: **At Night**

Where: **In a House**

Cathy: What will I be when
I grow up?
Will I fly like you?

Mother: You can't say now, Cathy.
You must go to sleep now.
I must go to work.
Father will be with you.

(*Cathy does go to sleep.*)

Cathy: Three, two, one! Up we go!
I can fly for my country at last!

(*Cathy looks at Bart.*)

Who are you?

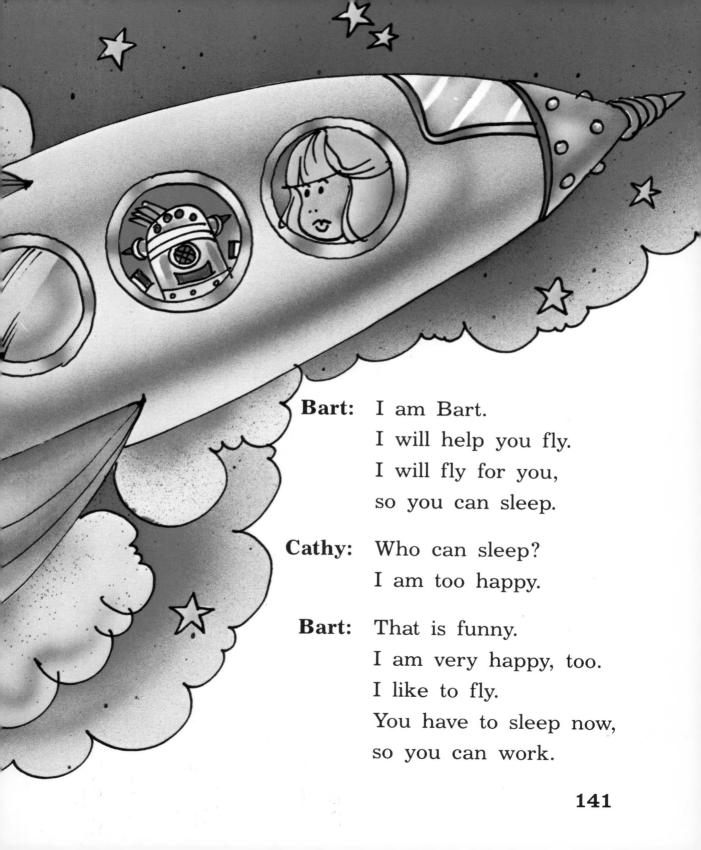

Bart: I am Bart.
I will help you fly.
I will fly for you,
so you can sleep.

Cathy: Who can sleep?
I am too happy.

Bart: That is funny.
I am very happy, too.
I like to fly.
You have to sleep now,
so you can work.

(That night at three, Bart calls to Cathy.)

Bart: Cathy, Cathy, get up!
Get up!
I can't get the drive box
to work!
It will have to work, or we
will go down.

Cathy: That is funny.
It must have run down.

Bart: I will kick the drive box,
and then it will work.
One, two, three—kick!

Cathy: Stop! Don't do that!
We must have the drive box
to fly.
What can we do?

Bart: We can't help it.
Look out! Down we go!

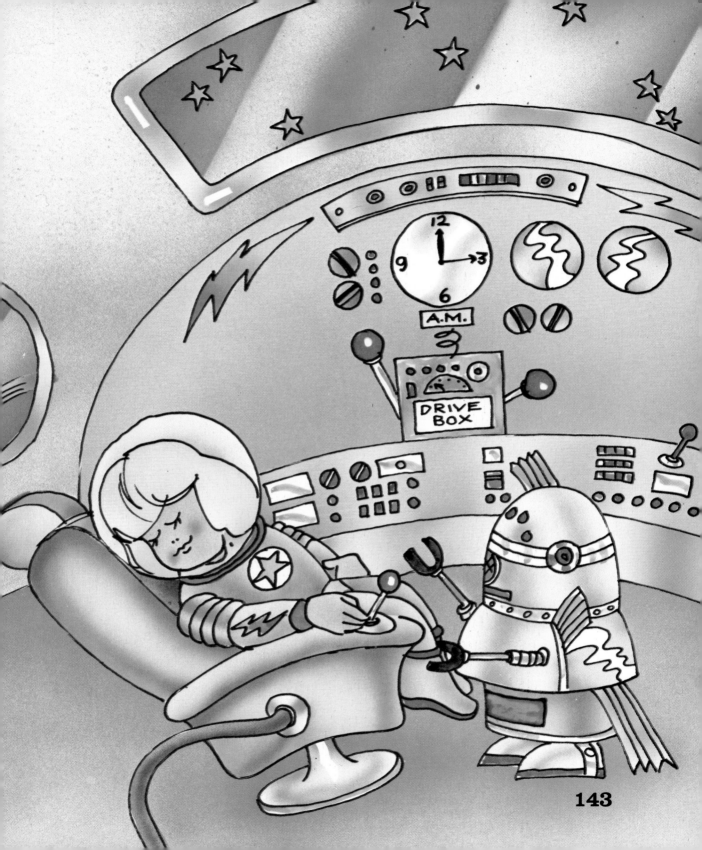

(Cathy and Bart get out. They are in a green country.)

Cathy: Where are we?
Why is it so green?
Who are you?

Tasha: You are in Green Country.
I am Tasha.
I live in Green Country.
Who are you?

Cathy: I am Cathy, and that is Bart.
We must get help.
The drive box does not work.

145

Tasha: What is a drive box?

Bart: The drive box is a little green
box that we must have to fly.

Tasha: So, it is green!
Then we can help you.
We will work on a green
drive box.

146

*(Tasha and some Green People work on
the drive box.)*

Tasha: Three, two, one!
Now your drive box will work.
You can fly now, but Bart
must not kick the drive box.

Bart: Very funny!

Tasha: I am happy that we have
seen you.
I am happy that you were in
Green Country.

Cathy: I am happy that I have seen
you, too.
I will write to you in
Green Country.
Bart will see that you get
the letter.

Bart: I will be happy to help.

(Cathy and Bart get in and up they go.)

(Cathy and Bart get out.)

Woman: Have you seen Green Country?

Cathy: I have seen Green Country!
Bart and I have seen Green
Country.
We liked it.

Man: You were the first girl to go
to Green Country.
What were the Green People like?

Cathy: The Green People were a big help
to Bart and me.
Bart and I will write a book
on Green Country.
We will take three trips to see
Green Country.

Bart: We will?

(Mother calls, "Time to get up!")

Cathy: That was funny!

I did not go to Green Country.
I did not see Green People.
I liked Bart.
But now I can say what I will be when I grow up.

When I grow up, I will fly for my country.

Questions

Read and think.

1. Where did Cathy and Bart fly?

2. What did the Green People do to help Cathy and Bart?

3. What will Cathy do for work when she is big?

SPACE SWING

When my swing goes up to the sky of blue,
I can touch the sun with the tip of my shoe.
Away up high where the white clouds race,
I play I'm an astronaut out in space.
I guess that a moon trip might be fun,
But here in my swing I can touch the sun.

Margaret Hillert

Picture Dictionary

Aa   **air**

Pam can jump up in the <u>air</u>.

am

Who <u>am</u> I?

apples

Jim likes <u>apples</u>.

Bb   **be**

The sky will <u>be</u> blue.

154

Bb

blue

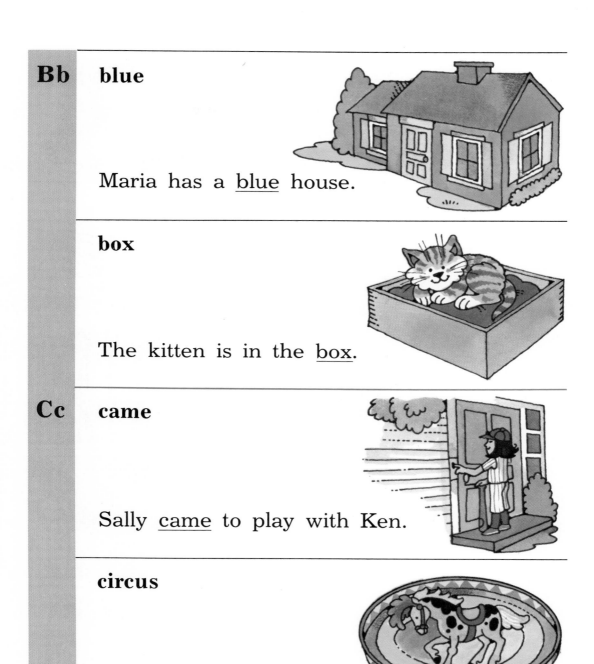

Maria has a <u>blue</u> house.

box

The kitten is in the <u>box</u>.

Cc

came

Sally <u>came</u> to play with Ken.

circus

I saw a pony at the <u>circus</u>.

Dd

day

It is <u>day</u>.

dear

Tim's letter said, "<u>Dear</u> Tim."

don't

"<u>Don't</u> take the ball!" says Sam to the dog.

drive

The woman will <u>drive</u> the school bus.

Ff

farm

Tim and Linda live on a <u>farm</u>.

F f

father

Father helps Linda read
a book.

first

Jane will go first.

fly

Mother will fly the plane.

friend

Ted is Nan's friend.

funny

Cathy looks funny!

Gg

giraffe

Look at the giraffe.

green

The bird is green.

grow

The kitten will grow up to be a cat.

Ll

last

Who will be last?

Ll

letter

Sue has a <u>letter</u>.

live

They <u>live</u> in the city.

looking

She is <u>looking</u> at the bird.

Mm

mail

Ted will <u>mail</u> a letter.

Mm

may

"May I pet your cat, David?" said Sue.

me

Look at me!

mother

Jim and Sally help my mother paint the house.

must

Anne must go home now.

Nn

night

It is <u>night</u>.

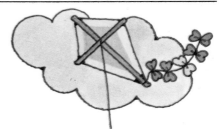

not

Kim is <u>not</u> happy.

Oo

of

I see the top <u>of</u> the tent.

one

<u>One</u> pony is in the truck.

or

Will it go up <u>or</u> down?

Pp

paints

Anne <u>paints</u> a bird.

pick

Can you <u>pick</u> out a pet?

pictures

Anne and Sue look at
the <u>pictures</u>.

pretty

"You look <u>pretty</u>, Sue,"
said the woman.

put

We <u>put</u> the apples in
the truck.

Ss

school

My <u>school</u> is big.

seen

"Have you <u>seen</u> Bart?" asked Father.

sit

Tim and José <u>sit</u> in the bus.

sky

A bird and a plane are in the <u>sky</u>.

Ss **sleep**

Maria will go to <u>sleep</u> now.

so

Mark sits on a box <u>so</u> he can see.

some

Tim can pick <u>some</u> of the apples.

spots

The dog and the bird have <u>spots</u>.

Ss **stop**

The bus will <u>stop</u>.

Tt **take**

Fred will <u>take</u> Jane to school.

teacher

My <u>teacher</u> helps me
at school.

teacher's

Mark has the <u>teacher's</u> book.

Tt

teaches

Lisa <u>teaches</u> Rosa to
play ball.

tent

A <u>tent</u> can be a house.

then

The cat and dog look.
<u>Then</u> they run after the ball.

they

<u>They</u> like to play.

Tt

three

Three fish jump out of
the water.

time

It is time to go to school.

top

A bird is on top of a house.

trips

We like to take trips to
the country.

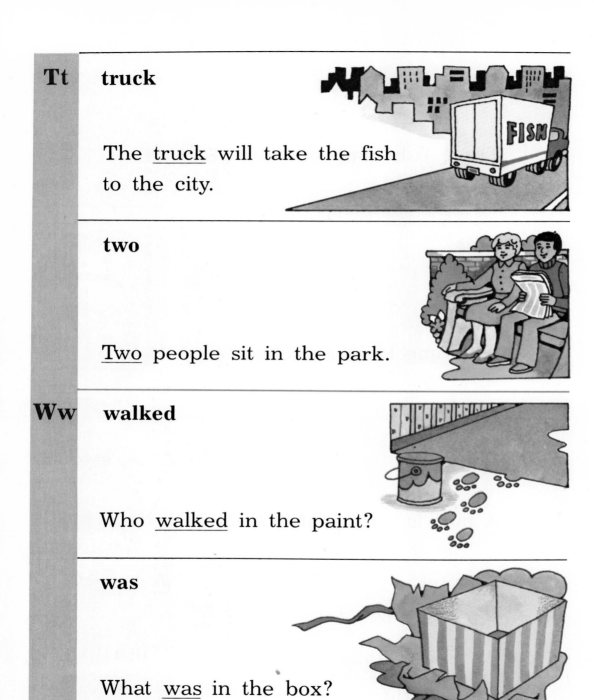

Tt

truck

The <u>truck</u> will take the fish
to the city.

two

<u>Two</u> people sit in the park.

Ww

walked

Who <u>walked</u> in the paint?

was

What <u>was</u> in the box?

168

Ww **water**

The <u>water</u> is blue.

were

"<u>Were</u> you in the paint?" asked Mother.

what

<u>What</u> is in the box?

when

Tim and Mark will fish <u>when</u> they get to the water.

Ww

why

Why can't they go out
to play?

will

Kim will get up now.

work

Anne and Sue work
at school.

write

José can write a letter.

Word List

Unit 1: Circus Friends

A Friend at School
12. friend
    school
13. Sue
15. Kim
    me
    Anne
    am

My School
20. work
    will
    Tim
    Jane
    they
21. stop
22. first

A Friend in the Country
29. must
    write
    letter
    Dear
    March
    José
    mail

A Circus School
40. circus
    giraffe
    not
41. then
42. sit